Matter & Materials

Grades 4-6

Written by Miranda Palmer
Illustrated by Ric Ward

ISBN 1-55035-675-5
Matter & Materials, SSB1-117
Copyright 2002 S&S Learning Materials
15 Dairy Avenue
Napanee, Ontario
K7R 1M4
All Rights Reserved * Printed in Canada
A Division of the Solski Group

Published in Canada by:
S&S Learning Materials
15 Dairy Avenue
Napanee, Ontario
K7R 1M4
www.sslearning.com

Published in the United States by:
T4T Learning Materials
5 Columba Drive PMB 175
Niagara Falls, New York
14305
www.t4tlearning.com

Look For Other Science Units

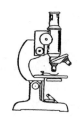

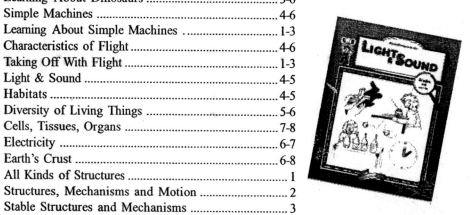
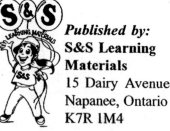
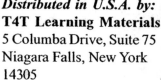

Published by:
S&S Learning Materials
15 Dairy Avenue
Napanee, Ontario
K7R 1M4

Distributed in U.S.A. by:
T4T Learning Materials
5 Columba Drive, Suite 75
Niagara Falls, New York
14305

SSB1-117

Matter and Materials

Table of Contents

Matter and Materials

Overall Expectations

Students will be able by the end of Grade Four to:

- demonstrate understanding that certain materials can transmit, reflect, or absorb light or sound;
- investigate materials that transmit, reflect, or absorb light or sound and use their findings in designing objects and choosing materials from which to construct them;
- explain why materials that transmit, reflect, or absorb light or sound are used in a variety of consumer products.

Students will be able by the end of Grade Five to:

- demonstrate an understanding of the three states of matter and of changes in state;
- investigate common changes of state (e.g. melting, freezing, condensing, evaporating) and make informed choices about materials when finding solutions to problems in designing and constructing objects;
- identify the properties that make different materials useful in common products and discuss the environmental impact of their use.

Students will be able by the end of Grade Six to:

- demonstrate an understanding of the properties of air (e.g. air and other gases have mass) and explain how these can be applied to the principles of flight;
- investigate the principles of flight and determine the effect of the properties of air on materials when designing and constructing flying devices;
- identify design features (of products or structures) that make use of the properties of air and give examples of technological innovations that have helped inventors to create or improve flying devices.

Specific Expectations

By the end of Grade Four students will:

- recognize and describe how different materials affect light (e.g. water and prisms bend light as it passes through them; mirrors and polished metals reflect light);
- classify materials (e.g. glass, clear acrylic) as translucent (e.g. frosted glass, white plastic shopping bags, tissue paper) or opaque (e.g. wood);
- demonstrate how opaque materials absorb light and thereby cast shadows;
- investigate, through explorations, ways in which different properties of materials, including their shape, affect the nature of sound (e,g, compare the sound produced by striking solid and hollow materials);
- identify and describe, using their observations, physical changes in a material that can alter the sound it makes (e.g. the differences in sound when a loose rubber band and a stretched rubber band are plucked);
- identify, using observations, a variety of materials through which sound can travel (e.g. by ringing bells under water; by sending messages along a string).

Matter and Materials

By the end of Grade Five, students will:

- identify and describe some changes to materials that are reversible and some that are not (e.g. freezing and melting are reversible; burning is not);
- describe changes they observe in the properties of materials when the materials interact with each other (e.g. when paints are mixed; when water is combined with gelatin;
- describe examples of interactions between materials that result in the production of a gas (e.g. antacid tablets in water, baking soda in vinegar);
- identify the three different states of matter—solid, liquid and gas—and give examples of each state (e.g. solid: sugar, rock; liquid: water, oil, gasoline; gas: water vapour, air, oxygen);
- identify the characteristic properties of each of the three states of matter and group materials on the basis of these properties (e.g. solids have definite volume and hold their shape; liquids have definite volume but take the shape of the container; gases have no definite volume and take the volume and shape of their container;
- recognize, on the basis of their observations that melting and evaporation require heat;
- use a thermometer to measure the temperature of a material;
- identify melting, freezing, condensation and evaporation as changes of state that can be reversed;
- describe, using their observations non reversible changes that occur when some materials are heated (e.g. when paper is burnt; when an egg is cooked);
- investigate and describe the changes in the relative volume, shape and temperature of materials when pressure is applied to them (e.g. the effects of using a hammer on clay or of sitting on a beach ball with the stopper removed).

By the end of Grade Six, students will:

- recognize that gravity does not depend on the presence of air;
- demonstrate understanding that gases expand to fill a space;
- demonstrate that air expands when heated (e.g. heat a garbage bag partially filled with air using a blow dryer);
- demonstrate and explain how the shape of a surface over which air flows affects the role of lift (Bernoulli's principle) in overcoming gravity (e.g. changing the shape of aeroplane wings affects the air flow around them);
- demonstrate and describe methods used to alter drag in flying devices (e.g. flaps on a jet aircraft's wings);
- explain the importance of minimizing the mass of an object when designing devices to overcome the force of the earth's gravity;
- describe the sources of propulsion for flying devices (e.g. moving air, propellers, combustible fuel);
- describe how unbalanced forces are used to steer aeroplanes and spacecraft (e.g. rocket firings to control docking in space).

Matter and Materials

Teacher Information

What is matter?

Matter is the substance of which all things are made. All objects are made of matter and may differ widely from one another. All objects have one thing in common–they all occupy space. Matter is defined by scientists as anything that occupies space. All matter has _inertia_. Matter is able to resist any change in its condition of rest or motion. The amount of matter in an object is called its _mass_. Scientists define mass as a measure of inertia. The earth's gravitational attraction for a given mass gives matter its _weight_.

Matter can be changed into _energy_ and energy into _matter_. Matter changes into energy when radium and other radioactive elements disintegrate and when atomic bombs explode. Energy changes into matter when subatomic particles collide at high speeds and create new, heavier particles.

The Properties of Matter

There are many varieties of matter and each variety possesses certain common characteristics. Each variety is recognized by its special characteristics or _properties_. These properties make one kind of matter different from others. Matter has two main types of properties--_physical_ and _chemical_.

Physical Properties:

Certain kinds of matter are recognized by our _sight_, _smell_, _touch_, _taste_ or _hearing_. Silver is recognized by its colour, salt by its taste and gasoline by its odour. These are examples of _physical properties_ of matter. Another property is the _matter's density_, the amount of mass for each unit of volume. For example, a block of cork weighs less than a block of common wood the same size. Another property is _matter's solubility_ which is its ability to dissolve. _Conductivity_ is a property that shows matter's ability to conduct heat or electricity.

Chemical Properties:

Chemical properties of matter show how a substance acts when it undergoes _chemical change_. For example, one chemical property of iron is its ability to combine with oxygen in moist air to form iron oxide or rust. Scientists call changes in the composition of matter "chemical changes". Changes that alter the value of _physical properties_, such as _weight_ or _density_, but cause no change in the composition of matter are called _physical changes_. For example, when water changes to steam it undergoes physical not chemical change.

Compounds and Elements:

Scientists are able to separate some substances into two or more simpler kinds of matter with new properties by using _chemical processes_. Such a substance is called a _compound substance_ or a _chemical compound_. Substances that cannot be broken down into simpler varieties of matter by chemical elements are called _elementary substances_.

Matter and Materials

Structure of Matter

Most matter is made up of _atoms_. An atom is the smallest amount of an element that can combine in a chemical reaction to form a _compound_. Atoms are made up of particles called _protons_, _neutrons_ and _electrons_. Protons and neutrons are made up of particles called _quarks_. Quarks are held together by particles called _gluons_.

All atoms contained in an _elementary substance_ have identical chemical properties. A _compound substance_ is formed when two or more elements are combined. The atoms of one substance combine with the atoms of another substance. These atoms from larger particles are called _molecules_. For example, two atoms of hydrogen and one atom of oxygen form one molecule of water. Atoms and molecules are extremely small and are impossible to count.

Compound substances may be _organic_ or _inorganic_. Organic compounds contain the element _carbon_. They are found in all living organisms. Organic molecules are among the largest molecules and may contain thousands of atoms. All other compounds are called _inorganic_.

Molecules are bound together by an _electrical force_. This force is produced by the _electrons_ in the _atoms_.

States of Matter

Matter usually is found in three physical forms–_solid_, _liquid_ and _gas_. For example, ice is a _solid state_ but when heated it melts at a definite temperature to form a _liquid_ called water. Heat also causes the temperature of the water to rise to a certain point; the water boils, producing _steam_, a _gas_. When the heat is removed the process is reversed. The chemical composition of water remains the same regardless of the changes it goes through. _Plasma_ is a fourth state of matter and exists only under special conditions.

Solids:

All solids have _form_, _hardness_ and _rigidity_ (the ability to oppose a change of shape). For example, a stone does not change shape easily. Some solids are _brittle_ and will _shatter_ when struck. Others have great _tensile_ strength and resist being pulled apart. Solids that are metals have _malleability_ (the ability to be beaten thin) and _ductility_ (the ability to be drawn into wires. The atoms in almost all solids are arranged in regular patterns called _crystals_.

Liquids:

Liquids have _no shape_ of their own. They _take on the shape_ of any container in which they are placed. They fill the container when their volume is the same as the containers.

Gases:

All gases have almost identical behaviour. They exert _pressure_ in all directions. All gases are _compressible_. Gases _expand_ and _exert_ pressure when they are confined.

Matter and Materials

Plasmas:

Plasmas are found in the interior of stars, in outer space, neon lamps and florescent lamps and in some laboratory experiments. Plasmas result when the atoms in a gas become ionized or electrically charged. Electrical forces between the gas atoms give the gas new physical properties.

Materials

Materials are solid substances from which many manufactured products are made. There are two groups of materials. They are _natural materials_ and _extracted materials_. Natural materials include stone, wood and wool. Extracted materials, such as plastics, alloys (metal mixtures) and ceramics are made through processing substances.

Materials are evaluated for their _properties_ (qualities) by manufacturers. Most properties of materials fall into six groups. They are _mechanical, chemical, electrical, magnetic, thermal_ and _optical_.

Mechanical Properties:

Some of the most important mechanical properties are _stiffness, yield stress, toughness, strength, creep_ and _fatigue resistance_. _Stiffness_ measures how much a material bends when first subjected to a mechanical force; for example, the degree a shelf first bends when a heavy object is placed on it. _Yield stress_ measures how much force per unit area must be exerted on a material for that material to permanently deform (change its shape). Materials that deform easily are usually not wanted. _Toughness_ measures a material's resistance to cracking. _Strength_ measures the greatest force a material can withstand without breaking. _Creep_ is a measure of a material's resistance to gradual deformation under a constant force. _Fatigue resistance_ measures the resistance of a material to repeated applications and withdrawals of force.

Chemical Properties:

Catalytic properties measure the ability of a material to function as a _catalyst_ (its ability to provide a favourable site for a certain chemical reaction to occur). _Resistance to corrosion_ measures how well a material holds up to chemical attack by the environment.

Electrical Properties:

Electrical properties are necessary in order to produce products designed either to _conduct_ (carry) or _block_ the flow of electrical current.

Magnetic Properties:

Magnetic properties show a material's response to a magnetic field; for example, that region around a magnet or a conductor where force of magnetism can be felt.

Matter and Materials

Thermal Properties:

Thermal properties reflect a material's response to heat. _Thermal conductivity_ measures how well a material conducts heat. For example, pots and pans must be made of materials that have a high thermal conductivity so that they can transfer heat to food. _Heat capacity_ measures a material's ability to contain heat. This property is important in the production of insulation materials.

Optical Properties:

Optical properties indicate how a material responds to light. The degree to which a material changes the direction of a beam of light going through it is important to the manufacturing of lenses for eye glasses. The lower amount of light the material absorbs, the more _transparent_ the material.

Natural Materials

Natural materials are usually used as they are found. They may be cleaned, cut or processed in a simpler manner that does not require much energy. _Stone_ and _biological materials_ are natural materials.

Stone:

Strong, hard types of rock are used as building stone. There are two types–_crushed stone_ and _dimension stone_. Crushed stone is mixed with tarlike substances to make asphalt, a paving material. It is also mixed with cement and sand to make concrete. Limestone and granite are found in crushed stone. Dimension stone is used for finishing and decorating buildings. Granite, limestone, marble, sandstone and slate are used as building stone.

Biological Materials:

Biological materials are substances that are parts of a plant or animal. Wood is an important biological material because of its _strength_, _toughness_ and _low density_. Thousands of products are made from wood such as houses, boats, furniture, and railroad ties. It is also a raw material for a wide variety of products such as paper, rayon and charcoal.

Plant fibres from cotton, flax and jute are used in their natrual state. Most plant fibres are _flexible_ and can be spun into yarn.

Leather is a _tough_, _flexible_ material made from the skins of animals. It is _strong_ and _durable_ as well. Shoes, belts, baseball gloves, baseballs, basketballs and footballs are made from leather. _Suede,_ a soft leather, is used for clothing.

Animal fibres are fur, wool and silk. Animal hair is found in fur and wool. These materials are excellent _insulators_ and are used for clothing. Silk is the strongest natural fibre and is made from silkworm cocoons. Clothing and decorative fabrics are made from silk.

Matter and Materials

Extracted Materials

Extracted materials are created through processes that require a great deal of energy or alter the microstructure of the substances. Extracted materials are _ceramics_, _metals_ and their _alloys_–plastics, rubber, composite materials and _semiconductors_.

Ceramic materials are brick, cement, glass and porcelain. They are made from clay, feldspar, silica and talc. Ceramic products include dinnerware, bathroom fixtures, building materials, insulators for electric power lines, windows and lenses for microscopes.

Metals such as copper, gold, iron and silver have been used for thousands of years by people. Today, metals are important in all aspects of construction and manufacturing. They are strong and good conductors of heat and electric current. Copper is used in its pure form in electric wiring.

Most _metals_ are too soft to use in their pure form so they are used as ingredients in alloys. Steel, cast iron and wrought iron are all alloys of iron and steel. Other elements mixed with steel give it such properties as resisting corrosion, increasing its hardness and making it more resistant to heat.

Plastics are _synthetic_ materials made up of long chains of _molecules_ called _polymers_. There are two types of plastics. They are _thermosets_ and _thermoplastics_. _Thermosets_ can be heated and set only once. They are highly resistant to heat and are used for electric parts, insulation foam, oven gaskets and appliance handles. Thermosets are also used in luggage and automobile parts. _Thermoplastics_ can be melted and reshaped. They are used much more widely than thermosets. Common products are telephone bodies, packaging and bottles.

Natural rubber comes from the juice of a tree. _Synthetic rubber_ is made from petroleum. Rubber is made of _polymers_ that stretch easily and then return to their original shape. This property is called _elasticity_. Rubber's elasticity is able to hold air and keep out water; its elasticity makes it tough. Tires, tubes and waterproof clothing are made from rubber.

Composite materials are made when various materials are _artificially_ combined to create new materials. They contain a large amount of one substance to which fibres, flakes or layers of another substance are added. _Fibreglass_ consists of glass fibres and a polymer such as _epoxy_. Fibreglass composites are used to produce products such as automobile bodies, fishing rods, aircraft parts, tennis rackets, golf clubs and plastics.

Semiconductors are materials that conduct electricity better than insulators, but not as well as conductors, at room temperature. Pure cells of semiconductor material combined with small, controlled amounts of other substances can perform many electronic functions. Silicon crystals are the building blocks of computer chips.

Bonding

Bonding is a force that attracts atoms to one another and holds them together. Such forces depend upon the _electron structure_ of the _atoms_. _Chemical bonds_ are either _ionic_, _covalent_ or _metallic_. _Ionic bonds_ are created by the transfer of electrons from one

Matter and Materials

atom to one or more atoms. The atom that loses electrons becomes a _positive ion_. The atoms that gain electrons become _negative ions_. In _convalent binding_, two or more atoms share pairs of electrons. A shared pair consists of one electron from each of two atoms. During _metallic bonding_, all the atoms in a metal crystal share electrons. The shared electrons are able to move freely throughout the crystal. The metal nucleus is surrounded and held together by the movement of negative electrons. _Physical bonds_ known as _van der Waals_ forces hold molecules together in a group. _Van der Waals_ forces are electrical forces carried by an interaction between charges of neighbouring molecules. They are much weaker than chemical bonds because no transfer or sharing of electrons occurs.

Teaching Suggestions

1. This unit was designed as a comprehensive junior unit covering many topics in matter and materials that are taught from grades four to six. Two different tests have been written so the teacher will be able to choose the areas that best apply to the particular grade. Methods of assessment may include formal testing, evaluation of experiment write-ups and anecdotal observations.

2. The unit begins with a review of the basic concepts learned in the primary division and encourages students to use investigative methods of discovery to find out the many properties of matter. Students are introduced to the scientific method and must use their skills of observation and drawing conclusions when experimenting with different materials.

3. Teachers may wish to have students create a vocabulary list at the back of their note books as well as a definitions page. Journaling is encouraged on a regular basis to help the students make connections between what they learn in the classroom and their world outside school.

4. Most materials for this unit are often readily available in a school; however, a few must be located or prepared ahead of time to be ready for student use. Begin collecting the following materials well in advance:

flashlight	plastic wrap	green garbage bag	coloured paper
balloons	eye glasses	yellow garbage bag	drinking glasses
golf ball	tissue paper	white garbage bag	glass pie plate
Epsom salts	contact lenses	clear gelatin	measuring cup
red jello	frosted glass	baking soda	food colouring
dry dirt	ice cubes	plastic containers	rubber band
sugar	icing sugar	coloured gelatin	icing sugar
a pail	baking dish	vinegar	computer paper

Matter and Materials

5. Teachers will need to take the first five to ten minutes to explain the input sections of each lesson and then explain how to do the activity. Unless otherwise specified, these activities are designed to be done as partners, in small groups or as whole class investigations.

6. Questions at the end of the activities may be used for class discussion or as homework assignments for the students.

7. In all cases, the activities are designed so the students may read the instructions themselves or the teacher may read them and help the students perform the activity or experiment step by step.

8. The vocabulary list may be reproduced for each student to use during dictionary work, writing sessions, word study activities and spelling lessons. The words may be written on charts to display in the classroom as well as for student use. The words may be discussed by the teacher with the students.

9. The cover page provided may be used along with the journaling page and colated with other activity sheets to make a Matter and Materials Booklet. The completed booklets may be put on display or sent home for parent perusal.

10. Set up a Matter and Materials centre in the classroom. At the centre, place books and magazines on the subject and various types of materials that may be used for classification and labelling activities. Encourage your students to add items to the centre.

11. Discuss the ways that materials feel. List the words on a chart.

   Examples: bumpy, flexible, furry, hard, heavy, slippery, rubbery, soft, spongy, wooly, rough, smooth, prickly, scratchy, lumpy, wrinkly, leathery, dry, wet, hot, cool, cold

   Make charts for how materials taste, smell, look and sound as well.

Matter and Materials

Vocabulary List

absorb	gravity	recyclable
affect	lift	reversible
angle	light	reversibility
appropriate	mass	shadow
Bernoulli's Principle	materials	shape
burning	matter	solids
chemicals	mix	sounds
compressed	mixture	space
conclusion	molecules	thrust
contracts	non-reversible	translucent
deflated	observation	transmit
drag	opaque	transparent
exert	oxygen	volume
expand	particles	
experiment	pattern	
flat	pressure	
flow	properties	
forces	reaction	
gases	recycle	

SSB1-117

Matter and Materials

Matter can be defined as anything that takes up space. There are three forms of matter. They are _solids_, _liquids_ and _gases_.

All matter is made up of tiny _molecules_. Individual molecules are too small to be seen by the naked eye. Molecules in a _solid_, like your desk or chair, are packed very tightly together, so there is very little movement and almost no space between the molecules. Molecules in a _liquid_, such as water, have larger spaces between them so they are able to flow. _Gas molecules_, such as the air we breathe, have large gaps between them. Gas molecules have no pattern to their movement and they bounce randomly off one another.

On the chart below, brainstorm and list different types of matter. Try to think of **ten** types for each one.

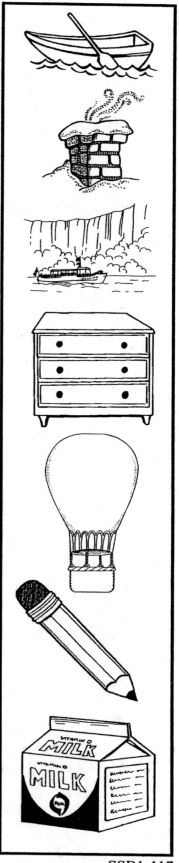

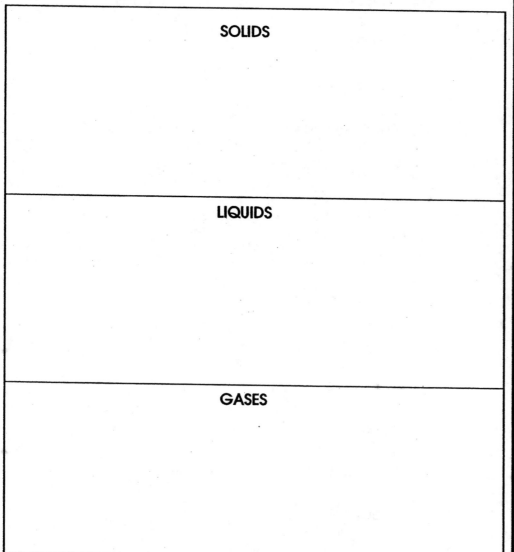

SOLIDS

LIQUIDS

GASES

SSB1-117

SOLIDS, LIQUIDS AND GASES

A) Draw a large picture in the box and label all the solids, liquids and gases in the drawing. Try to have at least three of each type of matter in your picture.

B) Can you think of something that can change from a solid to a liquid or a liquid to a gas?

_____

_____

_____

WHERE DO I BELONG?

Classify the solids, liquids and gases. Record the following words in their appropriate column;

desk   chalkboard   pop   steam   oxygen

juice   crackers   water   pencil   smoke

paper   ketchup   soup   fog   propane

exhaust   mustard   mist   dew   gasoline

milk   ruler   door   cup   carbon dioxide

helium   carpet

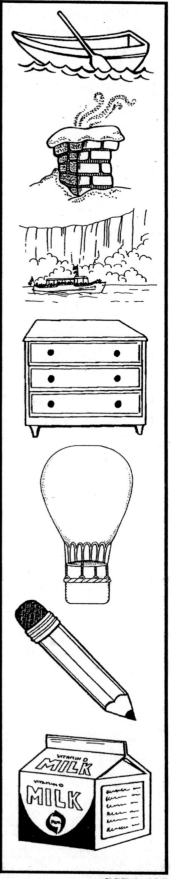

SOLIDS	LIQUIDS	GASES

SSB1-117

WHAT AM I?

A Solid, A Liquid or A Gas

Label the solids, liquids and the gases in the following picture. Expand the picture with other solids, liquids and gases.

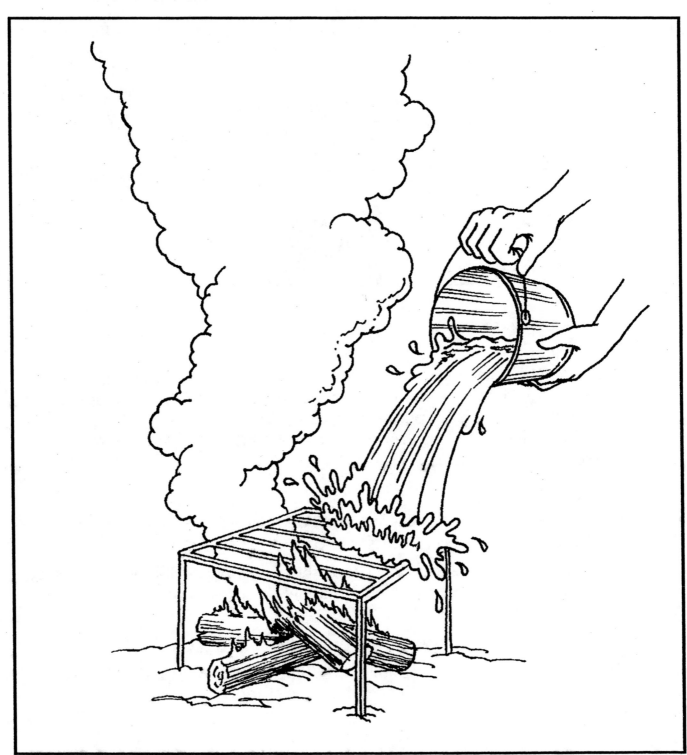

MATERIALS

Materials are _transparent_, _translucent_ or _opaque_.

Transparent materials can be seen through and transmit light; for example, a window.

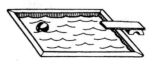    

Translucent materials transmit less light and are therefore more difficult to see through; for example, a white plastic bag.

Opaque materials cannot be seen through as they absorb all the light around them; for example, a book.

 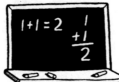  

Try this experiment.

You will need the following items:

- a flashlight
- ten to twenty various items such as plastic wrap, green garbage bag, yellow garbage bag, various sheets of different coloured paper, different types of paper such as construction paper, computer paper, etc., shoes, a jacket or shirt, a window, white plastic bags, books, balloons (both blown up and deflated), eye glasses, drinking glass.

Do the following things:

1. Try to look through the object. Can you see through it clearly? If you can, the material is allowing light to pass through it and the object is _transparent_.

2. If you can't see through it clearly or not at all, shine the flashlight through the object. Can you see the light? If you can, then some light is being allowed through and the object is _translucent_.

3. If you can't see any light or only very little, the object is _opaque_.

4. Record your findings on the chart entitled _"IS IT TRANSPARENT, TRANSLUCENT OR OPAQUE"_. Try to find at least five objects for each category. Some are easier than others!

  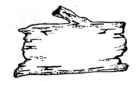  

IS IT TRANSPARENT, TRANSLUCENT OR OPAQUE?

ITEM	TRANSPARENT	TRANSLUCENT	OPAQUE

TRANSPARENT, TRANSLUCENT OR OPAQUE

Determine whether the following items are transparent, translucent, or opaque.

Sort them into their appropriate category.

window	glass of water	plastic wrap
air	white T-shirt	tissue paper
pencil	white shopping bag	ice cubes
desk	black construction paper	red jello
sand	contact lenses	text book
wood	frosted glass	overheads

TRANSPARENT	TRANSLUCENT	OPAQUE

Explain in your own words, using specific examples, the following terms:

1. Matter: _____

_____

2. Transparent: _____

_____

3. Translucent: _____

_____

4. Opaque: _____

_____

TRANSPARENT, TRANSLUCENT AND OPAQUE MATERIALS

In the following picture, label the _transparent_, _translucent_ and _opaque_ materials.

Expand the picture to include more of the three types of materials.

MAKE A TRANSLUCENT SURFACE

Materials:

You will need:

      1/4 cup of hot water

      a glass pie plate

      Epsom salts

Procedure:

1. Dissolve the Epsom salts in the hot water.

2. Pour enough in the pie plate to cover the bottom.

3. Set the pie plate in a warm place for about an hour.

4. Fill in the blank experiment sheet being sure to describe all sections fully.

 SSB1-117

EXPERIMENT RECORD SHEET

TITLE: _____

WHAT DO I THINK WILL HAPPEN? _____
_____

WHAT DO I NEED? _____
_____
_____
_____

HOW DO I DO THE EXPERIMENT? _____
_____
_____
_____
_____

WHAT DID I SEE HAPPEN? _____
_____
_____
_____
_____

DIAGRAMS

BEFORE	AFTER

CONCLUSION:
_____
_____

MAKING SHADOWS

Ever wonder why a window doesn't create a shadow but the window frame does?

The glass window is a _transparent_ surface which allows the light from the sun to go right through it. The window frame is usually an _opaque_ surface, such as wood or metal. Opaque surfaces absorb all the light coming from the sun and do not allow the light to go through it. By absorbing light, a _shadow_ is created.

Materials:

For this activity, you will need the following items:

- a flashlight
- a large sheet of white paper
- a pencil
- an eraser
- a ruler
- a book
- a pencil box

Procedure:

1. Place an object on the blank piece of white paper.
2. Shine your flashlight directly sideways at your object.
3. Draw the shadow that is created in the chart on the next page.
4. Now try shining your flashlight directly over the top of your object.
5. Draw what you see.
6. Now try angling your flashlight up and down on the object. Draw what you see.
7. When you have completed the chart called "MAKING SHADOWS", answer the following questions.

Questions:

1. Which was the best angle to get a shadow? _____

   _____

2. Which angle gave no shadow at all? _____

   _____

3. Why do you think there was no angle? _____

   _____

4. Which angle gave the longest shadow? _____

   _____

5. Which time of day do you think you would get the longest shadow? Why?

   _____

   _____

MAKING SHADOWS RECORD SHEET

ITEM	SIDEWAYS	OVERHEAD	ANGLED UP	ANGLED DOWN
PENCIL				
ERASER				
PENCIL BOX				
BOOK				
RULER				

 SSB1-117

WATERY MUSIC

Different materials produce different sounds when tapped.

Tapping your book with a pencil will make a sharp sound while tapping water with the same pencil will create a splashing sound.

In this activity you will create music using some glasses, water and a pencil

Materials:

You will need:

      five glass jars or drinking glasses (more than 1 1/4 cups in size)
      water
      measuring cups
      one pencil

Procedure:

1. Tap each glass or jar when empty and record the sound the jar makes. Does tapping the jar higher or lower change the sound? _____

2. Fill each jar with 1/4 cup of water. Compare the sound the jar makes now with the sound when it was empty.
   Record the comparison on the "WATERY MUSIC RECORD CHART"
   For example: Use the words - higher, lower, louder, softer

3. Add 1/4 cup more water to jars two, three, four and five. Tap each jar again.
   Record the sound comparisons on the "WATERY MUSIC RECORD CHART"

4. Add 1/4 cup more water to jars three, four and five. Tap each jar again.
   Record the sound comparisons on the "WATERY MUSIC RECORDCHART".

5. Continue adding 1/4 cup more water to jars four and five. Tap each jar again.
   Record the sound comparisons on the "WATERY MUSIC RECORD CHART".

6. Add 1/4 cup water to only jar five. Tap each jar again. Record the sound comparisions on the "WATERY MUSIC RECORD SHEET".

7. When you have completed the "WATERY MUSIC RECORD SHEET", line the jars up from least full to most full. Number the jars one to five from left to right.

8. Tap the following tune:

    3, 2, 1, 2, 3, 3, 3, 2, 2, 2, 3, 5, 5, 3, 2, 1, 2, 3, 3, 3, 3, 2, 2, 3, 2, 1

9. What tune did you just play?

_____

WATERY MUSIC RECORD CHART

JAR	EMPTY	1/4 CUP	1/2 CUP	3/4 CUP	1 CUP	11/4 CUP
1						
2						
3						
4						
5						

Create your own watery music. Write your tune on the line provided.

_____

_____

How did the amount of water affect the sound coming from the jars?

_____

_____

On your own:

Try this again using jugs and blowing into them. Now you are using a solid (the jug), a liquid (the water) and a gas (your breath) all together to make a sound.

MORE SOUNDS

In the following chart, use a pencil to strike the object, except number five which you will pluck with your finger. You will need to record the type of sound made.

OBJECT	SOUND	SAME	DIFFERENT
Flat Piece of Paper			
Crumpled piece of paper			

Empty glass			
Full Glass			

Deflated balloon			
Inflated balloon			

Golf ball			
Ping Pong Ball			

Loose rubber band			
Stretched rubber band			

MATTER

REVERSIBLE AND NON-REVERSIBLE PROPERTIES

Information Card

Matter is defined as anything that takes up space. It is interesting to note that matter can neither be created nor destroyed. Look at chalk, for example. Millions of years ago, tiny creatures lived in the ocean. When they died, their remains piled up. The enormous weight of the water in the ocean crushed these tiny creatures and turned them into a soft rock called limestone. This limestone, mixed with some other solid particles, is what makes classroom chalk. The chalk isn't created; it is simply a solid that has changed its form. When water boils away, the water has not been destroyed; it has changed form into water vapour, a gas. Later, that same water vapour may once again become water and possible turn into a solid in the form of ice.

Some changes made to different materials are reversible; some are not. The chalk will never again become a tiny sea creature, whereas ice will melt back into water again.

This is the principle upon which recycling works. Paper that has been used can be turned back into a pulp from which paper can be made again. Glass jars can be melted under extreme heat and can be formed into different glass shapes. The same is true for many plastics. Recycling is a good way to save our environment; it uses the reversibility of changes to matter to help cut down on pollution.

Some changes to matter, however, are not reversible. Burning wood and turning it into ash and smoke is not a reversible process. Other forms of matter that are involved in chemical reactions such as burning or reacting with acids are changed forever and cannot revert back to their original form.

MATTER

REVERSIBLE AND NON-REVERSIBLE PROPERTIES

Read the Information Card entitled *"Matter - Reversible and Non Reversible Properties"*. Answer the following questions with complete sentences.

1. Define matter.

   _____

   _____

2. How is it possible to create new materials but not new matter?

   _____

   _____

3. What does water become when it is frozen?

   _____

   _____

4. Is the answer from number three a reversible or a non-reversible change to matter?

   _____

   _____

5. State and explain an example of a non-reversible change to matter.

   _____

   _____

6. How does recycling use the reversibility of change to matter in order to save the environment?

   _____

   _____

7. Why do you think some materials are not recyclable?

   _____

   _____

MIXED-UP MATERIALS

Sometimes when two materials are mixed together, they combine to form something distinct and new. New matter has not been created, since no new molecules have been formed and matter can neither be created nor destroyed, but a new material has been formed from two different forms of matter.

In the following activity, you will be required to combine two materials together and then record (in the boxes provided) the changes that occur.

Materials:

You will need: clear or coloured gelatin, dry dirt, sugar, icing sugar, water, warm water, red, blue and yellow paint, bowls, popsicle sticks for mixing.

Note: Use no more than 50 ml of each when mixing.

Items to Be Mixed	Reaction (What happened/What was made)
sugar and warm water	
red and yellow paint	
red and blue paint	
blue and yellow paint	
gelatin and warm water	
dirt and water	
flour and water	
icing sugar and water	

 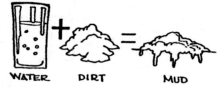

MIXED-UP MATERIALS

Collect other things that you would like to mix together.

Use the following chart to record the items that you mixed together and their reaction.

Try refrigerating the gelatin mixed with warm water. What happened?

Items to be Mixed	Reaction (what happened/what was made)

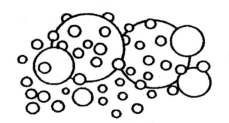
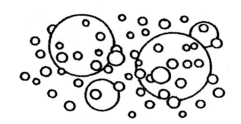

FIZZ

In this activity, you will be performing a chemical reaction which will result in the production of a gas.

Remember, the gas is not being created; it is simply the resulting change in two other combined forms of matter. This change is a _non-reversible_ change.

Materials:

You will need:

- a pop bottle or another bottle with a small mouth
- enough vinegar to fill half the bottle
- two to three tablespoons of baking soda
- a balloon

Procedure:

1. Stretch and pull the balloon well before you begin the experiment.

2. Half fill the pop bottle with vinegar.

3. Carefully pour in two to three tablespoons of baking soda.

4. Quickly stretch the mouth of the balloon over the mouth of the bottle and hold it in place.

5. Fill in the following page, recording your observations and conclusions after you complete the experiment.

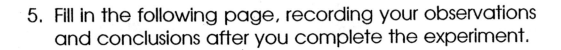

EXPERIMENT RECORD SHEET

TITLE: _____

WHAT DO I THINK WILL HAPPEN?

_____
_____

WHAT DO I NEED:

_____
_____
_____

HOW DO I DO THE EXPERIMENT:

_____
_____
_____
_____
_____
_____

WHAT DID I SEE HAPPEN?

_____
_____
_____
_____
_____

DIAGRAMS

BEFORE	AFTER

CONCLUSION:

_____
_____

MATTER AND VOLUME

Information Card

Everything we know is made up of *matter*. Matter is divided into three states: *solids*, *liquids* and *gases*. Solids are very densely packed *molecules* with extremely tiny spaces between them. Liquid molecules flow because there is more space between each molecule. Gases are made of molecules with relatively large spaces between them.

All *solids* are similar to each other in that they all hold their shape and have a definite volume. Hundreds of years ago, a man named *Archimedes* discovered that solids each have a certain, constant volume. His experiment went something like this. If you were to fill a pail with water and drop in a large rock, some water would spill over the side. No matter how many times you tried this experiment, the same amount of water would be spilled out using the same rock. The amount of water spilled is the volume of that particular rock or solid. If the rock or solid remains unchanged, the volume will always stay the same.

Liquids also have a constant volume but, unlike solids, they take the shape of the container they are in. A shovel put in a bucket stays the shape of a shovel. Water put in the same bucket will take the shape of the bucket. Therefore, two properties of liquids are they have a constant volume and they take the shape of the container that they are in.

Gases also take the shape of the container they are in but, unlike both solids and liquids, they have no definite, constant volume.

MATTER AND VOLUME

Read the Information Card entitled *"Matter and Volume"*. Answer the following questions with complete sentences.

1. How do the molecules of a solid differ from the molecules in a liquid?

   _____

   _____

2. Why are we able to move so easily through a gas such as air?

   _____

   _____

3. Why is it more difficult to move through water in a swimming pool?

   _____

   _____

4. What did Archimedes discover?

   _____

   _____

5. How did he prove his theory?

   _____

   _____

6. In terms of volume, how are solids and liquids alike?

   _____

   _____

7. Name two properties of liquids.

   _____

   _____

8. Name two properties of gases.

   _____

   _____

AIR VOLUME

In the following activity you will discover that air and water have the same properties.

Materials:

You will need the following:

- a water balloon
- a bucket
- a regular balloon
- some water

Procedure:

1. Before you begin, take note of the shape of each of the items in your list of materials, including the water.

2. Fill the bucket half full of water.

3. Blow three or four breaths into the regular balloon. (Do not fill it completely.)

4. Put a little water into the water balloon. (Do not fill it completely.)

5. Fill in the following observation chart.

ITEM	SHAPE BEFORE FILLING	SHAPE AFTER (SAME/DIFFERENT)
Bucket		
Water Balloon		
Balloon		
Water		

AIR VOLUME

In complete sentences, answer the following questions, based on the previous experiment.

1. Both the bucket and the balloons are solids. What must be true in order for a solid to change its shape?

_____

_____

2. Describe how the water filled the bucket.

_____

_____

3. Describe how the water filled the balloon.

_____

_____

4. Squeeze the water balloon. How does the water move within the balloon?

_____

_____

5. Squeeze the air balloon. How does the air move within the balloon?

_____

_____

6. How do air and water have similar properties?

_____

_____

CHANGING THE VOLUME

MAKE AN ICE SCULPTURE

In this activity, you will be creating an ice sculpture.

Materials:

You will need the following:

- plastic containers of various sizes and shapes
- water
- a place to freeze the water
- food colouring
- large, deep baking dish to store the sculpture

Procedure:

1. First, decide what shape or item you would like to make.
2. Next, mix water with a few drops of food colouring and pour into the container you have chosen.
3. Repeat until you have filled all the required containers.
4. Place in a freezer for twenty-four hours.
5. When frozen, remove the ice from the containers into the deep baking dish.
6. Form your sculpture.
7. You may wish to add paper accessories to your sculpture.
8. Leave it in the classroom for twenty-four hours.

CHANGING THE VOLUME

Answer the following questions with complete sentences.

1. What happened to the water when you put it in the freezer?

   _____

   _____

2. Did the water expand or contract? How do you know?

   _____

   _____

   _____

3. What happened when you left your scupture in the classroom for twenty-four hours?

   _____

   _____

4. In order to melt ice what do you need?

   _____

   _____

5. Is this process of freezing and melting reversible or non-reversible?

   _____

   _____

6. Illustrate your ice sculpture below.

AIR

Information Card

Air is all around us, pushing us from all directions. Air behaves a certain way under certain conditions. Because of its constant behaviours, scientists have been able to determine several properties of air. Some of these include:

- air has pressure

- air has mass

- air takes up space

- air can be compressed

- air expands when heated

- air is approximately 21 % oxygen

Air has the ability to move things up and down in any direction. Think of a T-shirt hanging on a clothesline in the summer. If there is no wind and the shirt is not moving, the air pressure pushing on all sides of the shirt is equal. If there is a wind it will cause the shirt to move because the air pressure is higher in the direction the wind is coming from. When there is a difference in pressure, there will be movement.

AIR

Read the Information Card entitled "*Air*" and answer the following questions.

Write a statement that makes the <u>false</u> sentences true.

1. Air pushes on us only from the east. _____

   _____

2. Air behaves a certain way under certain conditions. _____

   _____

3. When air pressure on a T-shirt hanging on a line is equal, it will move.

   _____

   _____

4. When there is a difference in pressure, there will be movement.

   _____

   _____

5. The phrase, "a property of air" means something scientists know to be true about air. _____

6. List three properties of air.

   _____

   _____

   _____

   _____

   _____

   _____

FORCEFUL CRAWLERS

Try this activity:

A. Crouch down on all fours on the floor.

B. Push as hard as you can on the floor.

C. Creep forward slowly, gradually increasing your speed as you cross the room.

1. What happened to the amount of pressure you were able to apply to the floor with your hands as you crossed the room?

   _____

   _____

2. Was the pressure applied to the floor when you were still greater or less than the pressure applied to the floor when you were moving?

   _____

   _____

3. Why do you think this happened?

   _____

   _____

   _____

BERNOULLI'S PRINCIPLE

Information Card

In the previous activity, you were behaving exactly the same way air or a liquid would behave if exposed to the same conditions. In the 18th century, a man named _Daniel Bernoulli_ discovered that fast-moving liquids and air exert less pressure than still or slow-moving liquids or air. This description of air is known as _Bernoulli's Principle_.

Why is this significant? Bernoulli discovered that this difference in pressure allowed for something called _lift_. Eventually, airplane designers used this principle to create an _airfoil_ and designed airplane wings that would allow an airplane to take off from the ground.

There are _four_ main forces acting on an airplane that cause it to move up, down or forward. These forces are:

1. **Thrust**: the force created by the engines to move the plane forward.

2. **Lift**: the upward force created by the shape of the aircraft's wings and the movement of air.

3. **Drag**: the resistance of forward movement caused by friction of air in its surface.

4. **Gravity**: the pull of the earth on a plane that gives weight.

Bernoulli's contribution, though seemingly simple, was extremely valuable in the development of the modern plane.

SSB1-117

BERNOULLI'S PRINCIPLE

Read the Information Card entitled "Bernoulli's Principle". Answer the following questions with complete sentences.

1. What is Bernoulli's principle?

   _____

   _____

2. How can you prove Bernoulli's principle to be true?

   _____

   _____

3. Why was his discovery so important?

   _____

   _____

4. What are the *four* main forces acting on an airplane?

   _____

   _____

5. Define the four main forces.

   _____

   _____

   _____

   _____

   _____

   _____

   _____

6. A difference in air pressure creates _____ .

BERNOULLI'S PRINCIPLE

Try this simple experiment that demonstrates *Bernoulli's Principle*.

Procedure:

1. Hold a piece of paper by the corners in front of your chin so the paper looks like this:

2. Blow over the top of the paper.

3. Answer the following questions based on this activity:

A. What does the paper do?

_____

_____

B. What did you expect the paper to do?

_____

_____

C. Describe the strength of the air pressure on either side of the paper before you began the experiment.

_____

_____

D. When you blew on the paper, how did the air pressure change (remember forceful crawlers)?

_____

_____

E. Was the air pressure higher or lower on the side of the paper that you blew on? How do you know?

_____

_____

DESIGN A FLYER

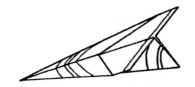

MATERIALS:

- one sheet of paper 8 1/2" by 11"
- crayons or pencil crayons
- tape

DIRECTIONS:

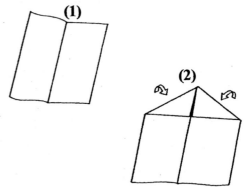

1. Fold your paper lengthwise (like a hotdog) in half and open it up again.

2. Fold the top two corners into the middle line you just made

3. Fold the same corners into the centre line again so you have a sharp point.

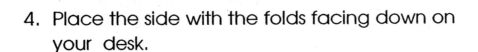

4. Place the side with the folds facing down on your desk.

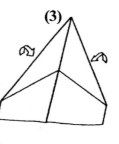

5. Fold the edges in toward the centre line so your flyer looks like a long triangle.

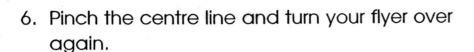

6. Pinch the centre line and turn your flyer over again.

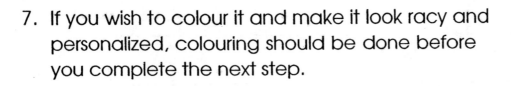

7. If you wish to colour it and make it look racy and personalized, colouring should be done before you complete the next step.

8. Place a piece of tape on the wings so your flyer doesn't separate.

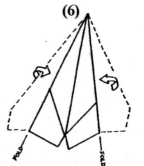

9. Now you are ready to test it.

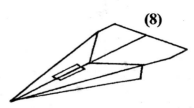

SSB1-117

RACY FLYERS

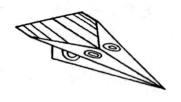

Using your flyer from the previous activity, test to see how far it will fly.

You will need a partner for this activity.

1. Partner A will toss his/her flyer **five** consecutive times, starting from a previously determined position such as a line of tape on the floor.

2. Partner B measures the distance the flyer went, using a standard method of measurement. Be sure to record the final measurement in metres and centimetres. Measurement is taken from where the flyer **LANDS**, not where it slides to.

3. Partner B retrieves the flyer and brings it back to Partner A. Once Partner A has tossed the flyer **fives** times, the roles reverse. **Record** your results in the following chart.

Partner A's Results

TOSS	DISTANCE
1.	
2.	
3.	
4.	
5.	

RACY FLYERS

 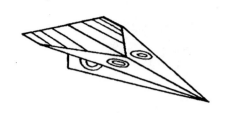

PARTNER B'S RESULTS

TOSS	DISTANCE
1.	
2.	
3.	
4.	
5.	

QUESTIONS

Answer each question with a complete sentence answer

1. Whose flyer went the furthest?

_____

2. How far was your longest flight?

_____

3. How long was your shortest flight?

_____

4. What was the average length of your flights?

_____

5. How could you change your flyer to make it go farther?

_____

_____

DESIGNING FLYERS
Now It's Your Turn!

- In this activity, you are required to design your own flyer.
- Write the instructions on how to build your flyer.
- Draw a picture of the final result.
- Test your flyer against other unique designs in the class.
- You will need to work with a partner.
- Write the instructions on how to create your flyer on the lines provided.
- Illustrate your flyer in the box provided.

HOW I MADE MY FLYER

_____

_____

_____

_____

_____

_____

_____

_____

_____

PICTURE OF MY FLYER

JOURNALING MATTERS

NAME: _____

WHAT I LEARNED ABOUT MATTER

_____

_____

_____

_____

_____

_____

_____

_____

_____

_____

_____

_____

_____

_____

_____

MATTER MATTERS!

WORD SEARCH FUN!

```
T  R  A  N  S  P  A  R  E  N  T  I  I  U
R  Q  O  M  Q  D  L  S  M  O  D  N  A  R
A  X  H  Y  M  T  P  W  A  J  M  D  J  L
N  F  E  C  B  A  O  D  E  G  H  I  Q  X
S  L  N  R  C  M  T  G  T  C  Y  V  C  N
M  O  L  E  C  U  L  E  S  W  E  I  Y  T
I  W  I  T  N  C  O  G  R  T  U  D  A  P
T  K  G  T  M  F  J  O  L  I  Q  U  I  D
G  O  H  A  I  M  G  O  I  G  A  A  I  F
G  U  T  M  Q  G  A  S  W  H  P  L  M  Q
Q  I  J  H  W  G  P  F  C  T  O  B  S  M
F  Z  P  T  N  E  C  U  L  S  N  A  R  T
```

FLOW	MATTER	STEAM	MOLECULES
GAS	TIGHT	OPAQUE	TRANSLUCENT
LIGHT	RANDOM	TRANSMIT	INDIVIDUAL
LIQUID	SOLID	MATERIALS	TRANSPARENT
SPACE			

SSB1-117

M-M-M-MATTER!

WORD SEARCH FUN!

```
R  F  E  L  B  I  S  R  E  V  E  R  R  I  N
E  U  X  T  U  N  O  I  T  C  A  E  R  J  I
V  J  P  H  R  Z  U  P  A  X  V  Q  K  D  T
E  N  E  G  N  C  X  L  I  E  X  C  C  E  A
R  U  R  I  I  N  N  F  R  X  S  R  H  S  L
S  G  I  L  N  R  O  S  P  I  F  E  E  T  E
I  A  M  H  G  D  I  O  O  H  A  A  M  R  G
B  F  E  S  O  B  S  E  R  V  A  T  I  O  N
I  F  N  A  I  S  U  F  P  B  N  E  C  Y  I
L  E  T  L  K  H  L  A  P  U  G  D  A  E  L
I  C  I  F  C  E  C  X  A  T  L  P  L  D  C
T  T  C  S  O  U  N  D  S  X  E  W  S  A  Y
Y  T  L  Q  S  W  O  D  A  H  S  B  D  H  C
U  L  Q  S  E  L  C  I  T  R  A  P  H  U  E
V  Z  M  W  X  S  C  B  P  Y  P  Z  R  L  R
```

AFFECT	DESTROYED	REACTION	REVERSIBILITY
ANGLE	EXPERIMENT	RECYCLING	APPROPRIATE
BURNING	PARTICLES	FLASHLIGHT	IRREVERSIBLE
GELATIN	REVERSIBLE	OBSERVATION	CONCLUSION
SOUNDS	CREATED	CHEMICALS	SHADOWS

     SSB1-117

AIR

WORD SEARCH

```
M F R E E Z E R U S S E R P A
T T T A D N A P X E X C P T E
F H C R E T A M I X O R P P A
I R A C L V L R M M O B D V S
L U R H W N O Q P P H A O C U
I S T I R S H R E U C L U S O
O T N M S B E R N O U L L I I
F E O E V S T E N M P O S Q R
R K C D S I N S E T S O H C A
I C N E E A T B U I Q N O N V
A U K S L A I R E T A M V U V
W B D P N D E F I N I T E E Z
M B R T Y T I V A R G Z L I H
F I A D C Y M R X W A A X O T
A Q G D I G A L G C K S Y W D
```

ACCESSORIES	COMPRESS	MATERIALS
AIR	CONSTANT	PRESSURE
AIRFOIL	CONTRACT	PROPERTIES
AIRPLANE	DEFINITE	SCULPTURE
APPROXIMATE	DRAG	SHOVEL
ARCHIMEDES	EXPAND	THRUST
BALLOON	FREEZER	VARIOUS
BERNOULLI	GRAVITY	VOLUME
BUCKET	LIFT	

SSB1-117

MATTER AND MATERIALS TEST ONE

NAME: _____

Answer the following as completely as possible.

1. What is matter?

_____

_____

2. Give two examples of each of the following:

solid: _____

liquid: _____

gas: _____

3. Explain how gas molecules move.

_____

_____

4. Fill in the following chart using the following items:

window, desk, construction paper, white shopping bag, red jello

TRANSPARENT	TRANSLUCENT	OPAQUE

MATTER AND MATERIALS TEST ONE

5. How is it possible to create new materials but not new matter?

    _____

    _____

6. Give an example of a reversible change?

    _____

    _____

7. Give an example of a non-reversible change.

    _____

    _____

8. List ten facts that you learned about matter and materials.

    _____

    _____

    _____

    _____

    _____

    _____

    _____

    _____

    _____

    _____

    _____

MATTER AND MATERIALS TEST TWO

NAME: _____

Answer the following questions as completely as possible.

1. Fill in the following "mixing chart".

ITEMS MIXED	REACTION (WHAT HAPPENED/ WHAT WAS MADE)
sugar and warm water	
red paint and blue paint	
flour and water	
gelatin and warm water	

2. What was produced when you mixed vinegar with soda?

_____

3. Solids _____ their shape and have a _____ volume.

4. Liquids take the _____ of their container and have a _____ volume.

5. Gases take the _____ of their container but have no _____ volume.

MATTER AND MATERIALS TEST TWO

6. Give an example of a reversible change.

_____

_____

7. In order to melt ice, you need _____.

8. List three properties of air:

   a) _____

   b) _____

   c) _____

9. What is Bernoulli's principle?

_____

_____

_____

10. When there is a difference in pressure, there will be _____.

11. Why was Bernoulli's discovery so important?

_____

_____

_____

MATTER AND MATERIALS

Answer Key

Matter and Materials (Page 14):

Possible Answers: Solids - desk, car, eraser, pencil, can, chalkboard, chalk, ball, bat, boat, etc. Liquids - water, milk, juices, cream, pop, freshie, tea, coffee, oil, gasoline, vinegar, lemonade, cider, syrup, ketchup, salad dressings, etc. Gases - oxygen, carbon dioxide, air, helium, smoke, exhaust, etc.

Solids, Liquids and Gases (Page 15):

A) Illustrations will vary   **B)** ice to water; water to steam

Where Do I Belong? (Page 16):

Solids: desk, chalkboard, crackers, pencil, paper, door, ruler, cup, carpet
Liquids: pop, juice, water, ketchup, soup, dew, mustard, gasoline, milk
Gases: steam, oxygen, smoke, carbon dioxide, fog, exhaust, propane, mist, helium

What Am I? (Page 17):

Pictures labelled should be logs - solid; grate - solid; smoke - gas; water in bucket - liquid; hands - solid; bucket - solid; earth or ground - solid.

Is It Transparent, Translucent or Opaque? (Page 19): Answers will vary.

Transparent, Translucent or Opaque (page 30):

Transparent: window, air, plastic wrap, contact lenses, overheads, glass of water
Translucent: red jello, white T-shirt, tissue paper, ice cubes, frosted glass, white shopping bag
Opaque: desk, pencil, black construction paper, sand, text book

1. Matter is anything that takes up space.
2. Matter that is transparent can be seen through and is able to transmit light.
3. Matter that transmits some light and can be seen through with some varying difficulty is said to be translucent.
4. Opaque matter absorbs light and cannot be seen through.

Transparent, Translucent and Opaque Materials (Page 21):

Articles that should be labelled are: window - transparent; curtains - opaque; T-shirt - translucent; tree - opaque; wind - transparent; leaves - translucent or opaque; branches - opaque; window frame - opaque; grass - opaque.

Making Shadows (Page 24):

1. The best angle was sideways.
2. The angle directly overhead gave no shadow.
3. The light was directed at an opaque object which absorbs all the light.
4. The sideways angle gave the longest angle.
5. Evening is the best time of day to get the longest shadow. In the evening the light comes mostly from a sideways angle.

Watery Music (Pages 26-27):
No
Mary Had a Little Lamb
The higher the water, the higher the sound.

More Sounds (Page 28): Answers will vary.

Matter - Reversible and Non-Reversible Properties (Page 30):

1. Matter is anything that takes up space.
2. Materials are made out of different forms of matter.
3. Water becomes ice when it is frozen.
4. It is reversible. It can melt back into water.
5. A non-reversible change is the creation of chalk. It is made of dead sea creatures and can never be made to live again.
6. We are able to change the material back into another form which can be used again.
7. They cannot be turned into something we can use; for example, smoke cannot be turned into a useful material.

Mixed-Up Materials (Page 31):

sugar and warm water - sugar dissolved
red and yellow paint - orange paint
red and blue paint - purple paint
blue and yellow paint - green paint
gelatin and warm water - gelatin dissolved
dirt and water - mud
flour and water - paste
icing sugar and water - sugar dissolved or turned into a paste, depending on amounts used

Matter and Volume (Page 35):

1. Solid molecules are densely packed. Liquid molecules have more space between them.
2. We are able to move easily through air because there is a lot of space between the molecules.
3. It is more difficult to move through water in a swimming pool because the molecules of water are closer together.
4. Archimedes discovered that solids have a constant volume.
5. He proved his theory by measuring the amount of water displaced by an object.
6. They both have a constant volume.
7. Liquids take the shape of their container and have a constant volume.
8. Gases take the shape of their container and have a changeable volume.

Air Volume (Pages 37 to 38):

Bucket: solid; round; same
Water Balloon: deflated, flat; different, (inflated)
Balloon: deflated, flat; different (inflated)
Water: shape of container; shape of container

1. It must be flexible.
2. It took the shape of the bucket.
3. It took the shape of the balloon.
4. It changes shape with the balloon.
5. It changes shape with the balloon.
6. They take the shape of their container.

Changing the Volume - Making an Ice Sculpture (Pages 39 to 40):

1. It turned to ice
2. The water expanded. The container cracked or the ice was coming out of the top of the container.
3. It melted.
4. You need heat to melt ice.
5. The process of freezing and melting is reversible.

Air (Page 42):

1. False. It pushes from all directions.
2. True.
3. False. Equal pressure means no movement.
4. True.
5. True.
6. Answers will vary.

Forceful Crawlers (Page 43):

1. It became less.
2. The pressure was greater when one was still.
3. As you move, the amount of force you are able to exert becomes less the faster you go.

Bernoulli's Principle (Page 45):

1. Fast-moving liquids and air exert less pressure than still or slow-moving fluids.
2. It was proven when the activity Forceful Crawlers was completed.
3. It helped in the development of the modern airplane and the creation of an airfoil.
4. The four forces are thrust, gravity, drag and lift.
5. Thrust is the force created by the engines to move the plane forward.
   Lift is the upward force created by the shape of the aircraft's wings and the movement of air.
   Drag is the resistance of forward movement caused by friction of air in its surface.
   Gravity is the pull of the earth on a plane that gives weight.
6. A difference in air pressure creates lift.

Bernoulli's Principle (Page 46):

A. The bottom end of the paper lifts up.
B. Answers will vary.
C. The air pressure was equal on either side of the paper before the experiment.
D. The pressure on the top of the paper became less.
E. The air pressure was lower because the air was moving faster and was therefore able to exert less pressure.

Matter Matters - Word Search

```
T R A N S P A R E N T   I I U
R Q O M Q D L S M O D N A R
R X H Y Q P W A J M I J L X
F E N C B A O D E G H D C Q X
L R C M T G T C Y I C Y A N
M O E C U L E S W E U I D C N T P
I W L T N C O G R T Q U I A I D
T K I T M F J O L I A L I M F Q
G O G A I M G O I G P A S Q
Q I H W G P F C H O B S M
F Z P T N E C U L S N A R T
```

M-M-M-Matter! - Word Search

```
R F E L B I S R E V E R R I N
E F U X T B N O I T C A E R J I
V J H U Z U P A X V Q K T
E N P G R N C X L I E X S D A
R U E I N N F S R I X F E L
S G R L G R I O S F O S R A E
I A M H O B S E R V A T G G
B F E A I S U L F P P B N N
I F N L K H L A P U E I L
L E T F C E C X A T X L C
I C S C L S O U N D S X A S Y
T T Q S W O D A H S B D E H R
Y L Q S E L C I T R A P H U U
U Z M W X S C B P Y P Z R L
```

SSB1-117

Air - Word Search

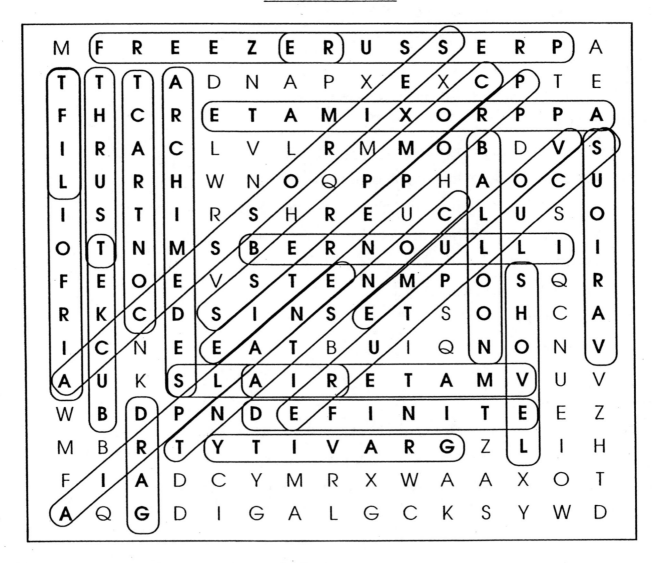

Matter and Materials Test One (Pages 55 to 56):

1. Matter is anything that takes up space.

2. Answers will vary.

3. Molecules move in a random fashion bouncing off one another.

4. Transparent: window

   Translucent: white shopping bag, red jello

   Opaque: desk, construction paper

5. Materials are made from changed matter.

6. A reversible change is one where ice turns back into water and then back to ice.

7. A non-reversible change is burning wood.

8. Answers will vary.

SSB1-117

Matter and Materials Test Two (Pages 57 to 58):

1. sugar and warm water - sugar dissolved

   red and blue paint - purple paint

   flour and water - paste

   gelatin and warm water - gelatin dissolved

2. A gas was produced.

3. Solids <u>keep</u> their shape and have a <u>constant</u> volume.

4. Liquids take the <u>shape</u> of their container and have a <u>constant</u> volume.

5. Gases take the <u>shape</u> of their container but have no <u>constant</u> volume.

6. Ice turning to water and then back to ice is a reversible change.

   (Answers may vary.)

7. In order to melt ice, you need <u>heat</u>.

8. a) Air takes space.

   b) Air has mass.

   c) Air has pressure.

   Answers may vary.

9. Fast-moving fluids, and air exert less pressure than still or slow-moving fluids or air.

10. When there is a difference in pressure, there will be <u>movement</u>.

11. His discovery helped with the invention of the modern airplane and the creation of an airfoil.